M000191305

This book is dedicated to:

© 2000 Havoc Publishing
San Diego, California
U.S.A.

Artwork © 2000 Robbin Rawlings Designs, Inc.
Text © 2000 Elena Luz Gómez

ISBN 0-7416-1147-3

www.havocpub.com

Made in China

Wishes

and

dreams

robbin rawlings

take advantage of the night
let yourself dream

I close my eyes to sleep
with great expectations

is what I dream
what I wish?

what comes first,
the dream or the wish?

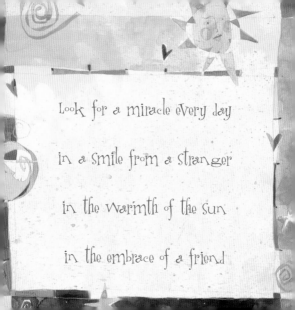

Look for a miracle every day

in a smile from a stranger

in the warmth of the sun

in the embrace of a friend

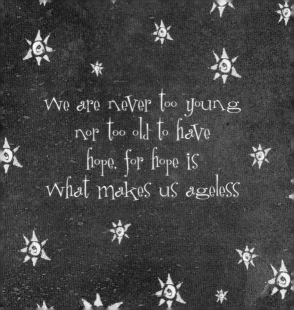

We are never too young
nor too old to have
hope, for hope is
what makes us ageless

everyone is
a miracle
waiting to happen

a dream, it came to me in sleep
one late september night
the memory of it I still keep
in my heart shining bright

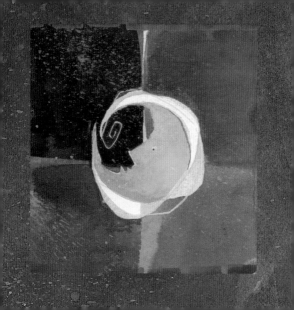

dreams are there
to speak to you
as you sleep

my dreams are a chance
to let me be

where I want to be
with whom I want to be

tread gently on your dreams

for they are just as much

a part of you as your

every breath

nothing perks up faith more than having a wish come true

go outside
I tell you
and soak up
the miracle of Nature

dreams are our daily rewards

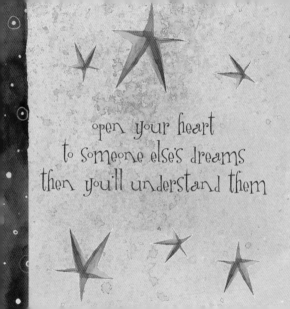

open your heart
to someone else's dreams
then you'll understand them

hope for the best
then expect it

wishes which benefit many

have a better chance

of coming true

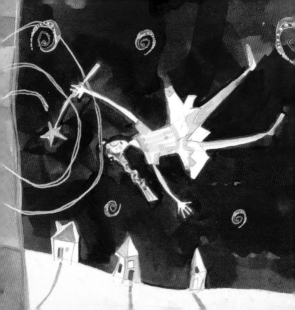

miracles come in all sizes
some the size of worlds,
some the size of fairy dust

then leave it alone
it will come true by and by

so many dreams

so many hopes

hard to tell

which I hold dearest

looking for miracles?
look into the eyes
of someone who
loves you

hopes are like

tender blades of grass

one must take care

not to step on them

as we grow
our dreams
get better

a miracle is a wish
wrapped up in layers
of hopes

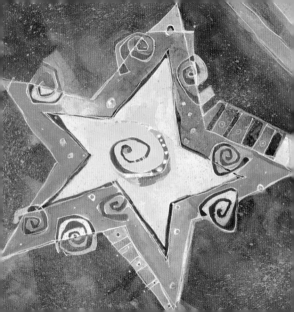

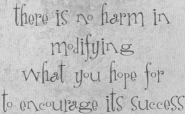

there is no harm in
modifying
what you hope for
to encourage its success

dreams were used
by great civilizations
as an ample source
of inspirations

have a broad view of the world
and you will see how your wishes
become more global

encourage your dreams
to go in only positive directions
don't dwell on the bad ones

keep track of what you wish

that way you'll know

when to celebrate!

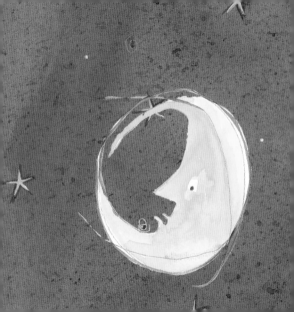

I wish for the simple happiness
of a child with a large
ice cream cone!

don't wander too far
from your hopes and dreams
for they will keep you warm
during your hardships

give your smiles away

for it may be all

some people

receive that day

count on your daily blessings

to keep your boat afloat

build a house of hope

and let your little miracles

shine through the windows

you will most likely not know

when someone wishes something

just for you

the answer is usually
riding in the wind
that toys with your hair

sneak into
people's hearts
with gentleness

pierce through the harsh exterior
of those inaccessible people

and you will find that they are
full of feelings, too

pretend to be content

even though you aren't

and soon you, too, will believe it

all over the world

people wish for the

same things

in different tongues

your dreams give insights
only you understand
so pay attention

the miracle of love

is that we are capable

of loving so many

different things.

and so many different people

sometimes what we
wish for
is too much like
what we want

keep your dreams in your mind

your hopes on your lips

and your intentions in your hands

an optimist is someone
who makes a wish
into an expectation

don't be afraid to let others
fulfill your wishes

always be true
to your hopes
and steady in what
you wish

take a chance
one does not attain
without risk

sweet dreams make

for blissful sleep

miracles live within us
we can make them happen

dreams are like pinholes
that let us peek into
our true wishes

I wish for a love as
true as the one
I would be

make your waking hours

as vivid as your dreams

I wish for a love as
true as the one
I would be

make your waking hours

as vivid as your dreams